GUINNESS WORLD RECORDS

RECORD-BREAKING COMPREHENSION

The
GREEN
book

Alison Milford

Published by

RISING STARS

in association with

GUINNESS WORLD RECORDS

Rising Stars UK Ltd.
7 Hatchers Mews, Bermondsey Street, London, SE1 3GS
www.risingstars-uk.com

Every effort has been made to trace copyright holders and obtain their permission for the use of copyright materials. The author and publisher will gladly receive information enabling them to rectify any error or omission in subsequent editions. All facts are correct at time of going to press. All referenced websites were correct at the time this book went to press.

Published 2013
Reprinted 2013

Published in association with Guinness World Records.

Author: Alison Milford
Text design: Burville-Riley Partnership/Fakenham Prepress Solutions
Logo design: Words & Pictures Ltd
Typesetting: Fakenham Prepress Solutions
Cover design: Burville-Riley Partnership
Publisher: Becca Law
Project manager: Tracey Cowell
Editor: Jennie Clifford

Photo acknowledgements
Page 8: © Roman Chmiel/iStockphoto; **pages 8 and 9**: © Nastco/iStockphoto; **pages 10 and 11**: © Dmitriy Smaglov/iStockphoto; **pages 22 and 23**: © John Woodcock/iStockphoto; **page 24**: © Egon/ iStockphoto; **page 30**: © Anneclaire Le Royer/iStockphoto; **pages 30 and 31**: © Ricardo Reitmeyer/ iStockphoto; **page 34**: © Josh Blake/iStockphoto; **page 36**: © Petek Arici/iStockphoto; **pages 42 and 43**: © Richard Goerg/iStockphoto; **page 48**: © Benjamin Jordan. **Rising Stars is grateful to Guinness World Records for supplying all of the record-related pictures in the book.**

British Library Cataloguing in Publication Data.
A CIP record for this book is available from the British Library.

ISBN: 978-0-85769-563-5

Printed by Craft Print International Limited, Singapore

CONTENTS

HOW TO USE THIS BOOK

Record-Breaking Comprehension features some of the most fascinating, weird and wonderful records from the Guinness World Records archive.

In this book, you will:

- read the exciting record-breaking stories
- practise and improve your comprehension skills
- go beyond the record to find out more.

The text

Each record or topic is described using a fiction or non-fiction text type, including newspaper reports, instructional web pages, blog entries and letters.

RECORD-BREAKING COMPREHENSION

DEEPEST UNDERWATER POSTBOX

POST CARD

Dear Tom   7 March 2012

I'm finally here on my deep-sea diving holiday in the beautiful waters of Susami Bay, Wakayama-Ken in Japan. Yesterday I saw an odd box. I thought it was sunken treasure but when I got closer I found it was a postbox! Will find out more and let you know.

From Dan

WATERPROOF POST CARD

Dear Tom   9 March 2012   Mr. To

This waterproof plastic postcard was given to me by the local post office to use in the underwater postbox. Since 23 April 1999 it has held the Guinness World Record for the world's deepest underwater postbox. I am not surprised. It is 10 m down! Wish you were here.

From Dan

18 W
Woki
Berks

WATERPROOF POST CARD

Dear Tom   11 March 2012   Mr. Tom V

Today I dived into Susami Bay but instead of seeing colourful fish I swam into a postman! It seems he dives down to the postbox every day and opens it up with a plastic key. On busy days, there can be up to 200 postcards posted by divers. It's a good job that fish can't read!

From Dan

18 Wilso
Wokingha
Berkshire

Wish you were here

8

Questions

Answer the questions to help you practise and improve your reading comprehension skills.

For help on answering questions, see pages 6–7.

The questions cover a range of different reading skills. For more information on these skills, see page 56.

Deepest underwater postbox

ON YOUR MARKS

a. Where is the world's deepest underwater postbox?

b. Why do you think Dan was surprised to see a postbox?

c. Why would Dan need a waterproof postcard?

GET SET

a. When did the world's deepest underwater postbox become a record holder?

b. Why do you think Dan thought the postbox was sunken treasure?

c. Do you think Dan is enjoying his holiday? Why?

GO FOR GOLD!

a. How many postcards can be posted on a busy day?

b. Why does the postman need a plastic key for the postbox?

c. Why do you think there is a postbox so deep underwater?

BEYOND THE RECORD

Use two sources of information to find out more about unusual postboxes in the world. Where are they? Who uses them? Who picks up the post? Use the information to create a fact sheet and remember to record where you found the information.

Beyond the record

In this section you will be asked to find out more about a record or topic and present your findings. This might be by using books or the internet.

9

READING COMPREHENSION

Reading the text

Read the text carefully. Don't rush. Try to immerse yourself in the information and enjoy it.

When you have finished, take a moment to reflect and think about what you have read. What was the author's purpose? Did the text make sense? Was there anything you didn't understand?

The questions

Always read the questions carefully before you begin to write. Then you will understand what you are being asked to do.

The questions check that you can:

- make sense of what you are reading
- find information and ideas in the text
- work out what the author means
- understand why a text is organised in a particular way
- comment on vocabulary and style
- say how a text makes you feel
- link what you read to your own life.

Answering the questions

Read the instructions carefully before you start to answer, as they give you information about how to answer the questions. Don't rush your answer.

Remember to refer to the text. You do not need to answer any questions from memory.

READING BETWEEN THE LINES

An author doesn't always tell you exactly what is happening. He or she often gives you clues to help you work it out for yourself.

Read the text below and then look at the worked question examples underneath.

Woofs and wags abounded at the annual Summer Fair. There were 15 entrants who competed for the Toss and Fetch Cup. This was won by Andy May and Buster. Buster caught one disc as many times as Andy could throw it in 60 seconds. He gained extra points by making several mid-air catches and was awarded a respectable 9.5 points.

Another duo, Misty and Olivia, hope to go on to international competitions.

'We are practising hard to get Misty holding more discs and want to try for the Guinness World Record,' said proud owner Olivia.

a. How many entrants were in the competition?

The answer can be found in the text itself – 15.

b. What or who is Buster?

The text doesn't actually say, but from reading the clues ('Woofs and wags', 'Toss and Fetch Cup') it becomes clear that Buster is a dog.

c. How did Misty's owner feel about her dog's success?

Again, the text doesn't actually say, but you can draw your own conclusion from the text: '"We are practising hard to get Misty holding more discs and want to try for the Guinness World Record," said proud owner Olivia' implies that Olivia is very pleased with Misty's success.

DEEPEST UNDERWATER POSTBOX

POST CARD

Dear Tom   7 March 2012

I'm finally here on my deep-sea diving holiday in the beautiful waters of Susami Bay, Wakayama-Ken in Japan. Yesterday I saw an odd box. I thought it was sunken treasure but when I got closer I found it was a postbox! Will find out more and let you know.

From Dan

WATERPROOF POST CARD

Dear Tom   9 March 2012   Mr. Tom

This waterproof plastic postcard was given to me by the local post office to use in the underwater postbox. Since 23 April 1999 it has held the Guinness World Record for the world's deepest underwater postbox. I am not surprised. It is 10 m down! Wish you were here.

18 W
Woki
Berks

From Dan

WATERPROOF POST CARD

Dear Tom   11 March 2012

Today I dived into Susami Bay but instead of seeing colourful fish I swam into a postman! It seems he dives down to the postbox every day and opens it up with a plastic key. On busy days, there can be up to 200 postcards posted by divers. It's a good job that fish can't read!

Mr. Tom
18 Wilso
Wokingha
Berkshire

From Dan

Wish you were here

ON YOUR MARKS

a. Where is the world's deepest underwater postbox?

b. Why do you think Dan was surprised to see a postbox?

c. Why would Dan need a waterproof postcard?

GET SET

a. When did the world's deepest underwater postbox become a record holder?

b. Why do you think Dan thought the postbox was sunken treasure?

c. Do you think Dan is enjoying his holiday? Why?

GO FOR GOLD!

a. How many postcards can be posted on a busy day?

b. Why does the postman need a plastic key for the postbox?

c. Why do you think there is a postbox so deep underwater?

BEYOND THE RECORD

Use two sources of information to find out more about unusual postboxes in the world. Where are they? Who uses them? Who picks up the post? Use the information to create a fact sheet and remember to record where you found the information.

Dubai Police News

25 January 2010

On 17 January 2010, the Dubai Police Force unveiled a mosaic made entirely of seashells. The mosaic was created to mark His Highness Sheikh Mohammad Bin Rashid Al Maktoum's fourth year as ruler of Dubai, United Arab Emirates.

It took 130 people (Dubai police officers and members of the public) 45 days to make the mosaic. First, they had to collect seashells from the local beaches and then they had to sort the seashells.

The seashells were laid carefully to form a picture of a dhow (boat) sailing on the sea. A dhow forms part of the Dubai police logo.

The finished mosaic was 13.81 m long and 12.62 m wide and was made from 59,835 seashells. A certificate was presented to the police chief to confirm that the Dubai Police (UAE) had set the Guinness World Record for the largest seashell mosaic.

ON YOUR MARKS

a. How many police officers and members of the public helped make the seashell mosaic?

b. Why did the seashells have to be sorted?

c. How would you feel if you had helped make the mosaic?

GET SET

a. How many seashells were used in the mosaic?

b. How do you think the Dubai Police Force feel about the ruler of Dubai?

c. Why do you think it took so long to make the mosaic?

GO FOR GOLD!

a. What is a 'dhow'?

b. What do you think 'unveiled' means?

c. Why was the mosaic design chosen?

BEYOND THE RECORD

Read the text again and make notes on the different stages of how the seashell mosaic was made. Choose a way to present this information to others – for example, on a flow chart, a poster with diagrams and captions, or a presentation on a computer.

OLDEST WING WALKER

Wing walking

On 30 May 2012, Thomas Lackey from the UK broke the Guinness World Record for the oldest wing walker. He was 92 years and 9 days old. He completed the wing walk at Gloucester Airport, Staverton. It lasted 10 minutes, 57 seconds.

Magnificent man *on* a flying machine.

What is wing walking?
Wing walking is when someone moves or stands on the wing of a plane while it is flying.

How did it start?
The first wing walker was an American called Ormer Locklear. During World War I, he would climb onto the wings of a flying plane to fix it. After the war, crowds came to see him perform amazing wing-walking stunts in Texas, USA. He died in 1920, aged 28, while performing a flying stunt for a film.

Stunts and flying circuses – how has wing walking changed?
In the 1920s and 1930s, the stunts that wing walkers performed became more daring. For instance, they did handstands, moved from one plane to another, played tennis and danced – all while the plane was flying! Many wing walkers joined flying circuses that put on exciting air acts. It was very dangerous and many lost their lives. From the 1970s, it was decided that wing walkers had to be tied to the plane.

ON YOUR MARKS

a. Who is the world's oldest wing walker?

b. Why do you think many wing walkers died?

c. Do you think Thomas Lackey was brave? Why?

GET SET

a. When did Thomas Lackey break this record?

b. Why did Ormer Locklear first wing walk and why did he choose to carry on?

c. Why do you think wing walkers now have to be tied to a plane?

GO FOR GOLD!

a. Write down three stunts that wing walkers used to perform.

b. What does the word 'daring' mean?

c. Imagine you are wing walking. Write down five adjectives to describe how you feel.

BEYOND THE RECORD

Use the internet to find out more about wing walking as a hobby. Plan the content for a wing-walking web page. Include information about the:

- wing-walking teachers
- pilots
- planes
- cost
- stunts.

YOUNG FOSSIL HUNTERS WANTED!

Fossils are the remains of creatures that lived in the distant past. Fossils are fascinating. They can tell us about the history of life on Earth.

A visit to the Jurassic Coast is planned for the next science field trip.

You will need:
- warm, waterproof clothes
- strong, non-slip boots or shoes
- a notebook and pencil
- a plastic bag in case the weather is wet.

Anyone interested in becoming a fossil hunter is welcome.

Special equipment (geological hammers, picks, goggles and gloves) will be provided by the school.

Some fossils, such as belemnites and ammonites, are very small. Others are very big, like the fossils of the Sinosauropteryx!

The largest ever Sinosauropteryx fossil found was 3.8 m long. The skull alone measured 60 cm!

The fossil is kept at the Shandong Tianyu Natural History Museum in Shandong province, China.

What will you find out about the history of life on this trip?
Places are limited. Get your name down today!

ON YOUR MARKS

a. What are fossils?

b. Why might you need waterproof clothes?

c. What might you use a plastic bag for on this trip?

GET SET

a. Where are the fossil hunters going for the school trip?

b. Why is special equipment being provided for them?

c. What effect does the author want the last line to have on readers?

GO FOR GOLD!

a. Where is the largest Sinosauropteryx fossil kept?

b. What does the phrase 'distant past' mean?

c. How does the poster encourage readers to go on the trip?

BEYOND THE RECORD

Use the internet or an atlas to find where the Jurassic Coast is. Find out why it was given this name.

Sightseeing – Northern Greece

Xanthi's Carnival and Mask

Xanthi is an old city in the north of Greece. It is famous for its carnival and for holding the Guinness World Record for the largest mask.

Every February or March, the local people put on costumes and masks, and walk or dance in a huge parade through the city streets. Some people even ride on colourful floats.

Largest mask

During the 2011 carnival, an artist named Fotis Stergiou made a huge mask of a Greek story character called Karagiozis.

Fotis started by cutting out 150 pieces of blue and white Styrofoam, which

is light and flexible. This took him four weeks. Then, with a team of 10 people, he spent eight days sticking the pieces together. Finally, he carved out the back of the mask and holes for the eyes and mouth.

On 5 March 2011, the mask was unveiled at the Filippos Amiridis athletic sport centre in Xanthi. It was 12.70 m high and 8.50 m wide, and covered 72.29 m² of floor space.

112

ON YOUR MARKS

a. Where is Xanthi?

b. If you were at the Xanthi carnival, who or what would you dress up as? Why?

c. Why do you think the artist chose to make a record-breaking mask?

GET SET

a. What was the mask made of?

b. Why did it take so long to make the mask?

c. Why was the mask made from something light and flexible?

GO FOR GOLD!

a. What were the main steps of making the mask?

b. Why do you think the mask was unveiled in a sports centre?

c. Why do you think the artist chose to create a mask of a story character?

BEYOND THE RECORD

Find three very different types of mask that have been worn by different people for different purposes. What mask would you like to wear and what would you do when wearing it?

Narrowest street

Thomas Parks

This month, we're exploring the smallest streets in Europe. Do you know a street that beats these? Then get in touch!

Spreuerhofstrasse, Reutlingen, Baden-Württemberg, Germany

In February 2006, Spreuerhofstrasse became the Guinness World Record holder for the narrowest street in the world. It is a mere 31 cm at its narrowest point and only 50 cm at its widest point – a tight squeeze after a large lunch! In 1726, a large fire in the city burned down many of the houses that were built up against each other. As a result, new houses were built with gaps between them, creating the narrowest street in the world.

Parliament Street, Exeter, Devon, England

Parliament Street is only 64 cm at its narrowest point and 1.22 m at its widest point. For over 600 years, people have used it to walk from Waterbeer Street to the High Street. In 1836, the people who lived on Waterbeer Street asked for it to be widened, but nothing was done and it has stayed narrow ever since.

Get streetwise to the narrowest street in the world: Spreuerhofstrasse, Reutlingen.

22 *World Traveller*

ON YOUR MARKS

a. What is the name of the world's narrowest street?

b. Why is it hard to walk down?

c. Do you think Spreuerhofstrasse should be called a street?

GET SET

a. How narrow is the world's narrowest street?

b. Why do you think gaps were made between the new houses?

c. Why do you think people use Parliament Street in Exeter?

GO FOR GOLD!

a. What destroyed many houses in 1726?

b. What do you think 'a tight squeeze after a large lunch' means?

c. If you lived on Parliament Street, how would you feel about making it wider?

BEYOND THE RECORD

Imagine you are a film director trying to find a narrow street to use in a spooky scene. What three questions would you ask about Spreuerhofstrasse? Who would you ask?

19

[Cut to Tim in the studio]

Tim:

Have you ever tried to balance a spoon on your face? Aaron Caissie, from Winnipeg in Canada, says the trick is to breathe on the spoon before you stick it on. He should know because on 18 April 2009 he became a Guinness World Record holder for balancing 17 soup spoons on his face. Seventeen spoons! That's amazing!

Aaron, who was 10, read about Joe Allison, a nine-year-old British boy who held the record for balancing 16 spoons on his face. Aaron decided to try to beat it.

After months of hard work, Aaron went on the TV show *Lo Show dei Record* in Milan, Italy, and broke the record by just one more spoon.

If you want to have a go at breaking Aaron's record, you need to know the rules:

• All the spoons need to be the same sort.
• Pick up and place each spoon on your face without help from anyone else.
• Do not use anything at all to stick on the spoons.
• Put the spoons on parts of your face, i.e. your ears, forehead, cheeks, nose, chin, mouth and eyes.
• Do not lean your face back.
• Keep all of the spoons on your face for **five seconds**.

Happy spoon balancing!

[Cut to Chan in the garden]

Tim

Here's the script for today's show. See you in rehearsal.

M

ON YOUR MARKS

a. How many spoons did Aaron put on his face?

b. Why would you want to try to break the record?

c. Why shouldn't you lean your face back?

GET SET

a. On which TV show did Aaron break the record?

b. Why are the rules set out as bullet points?

c. Why do you think Aaron used soup spoons for his record attempt?

GO FOR GOLD!

a. Who held the record before Aaron Caissie?

b. How do you think Aaron felt about attempting the record on TV?

c. Why are brackets used at the end of the script?

BEYOND THE RECORD

Plan your own balancing challenge. Write a set of rules and tips. How will you present the information to your group or class?

www.bloggingforlife.com/Ella_Smith2/

NOV 6	November 6, 2011 20:06 GMT
	Posted by **Ella Smith**

Q Search

January

February

March

April

May

June

July

August

September

October

November

December

Most consecutive haircuts by a team in eight hours

This team are a cut above the rest.

Today was really exciting! Mum was part of a team of hairdressers who tried to beat the Guinness World Record for the most consecutive haircuts in eight hours. (I looked up the word 'consecutive' – it means one after another.)

Early this morning, we went to the hair salon, Cre8, which is in Cape Coral, Florida, USA, to get ready and put out all the scissors and combs.

Then we opened the door for the long queue of family, friends and local people who had come to get their hair cut. I was the first one to sit down and then people just kept coming! It was like a party. There was even food and music!

Finally, just after 6pm, the team stopped. They had finished an amazing 307 haircuts in eight hours. Only 294 of those cuts were allowed but Cre8 still became the new world record holders!

Mum is very tired and her hands are sore, but it was worth it.

ON YOUR MARKS

a. Who came to have their hair cut?

b. Why did the salon need getting ready?

c. How do you think the writer felt about the day?

GET SET

a. Where is the Cre8 Salon?

b. Why was the day 'like a party'?

c. Why do you think some of the haircuts were not counted at the end?

GO FOR GOLD!

a. What does the word 'consecutive' mean?

b. Why do you think the writer is writing about the event?

c. Write down two reasons why you would have gone to get your hair cut.

BEYOND THE RECORD

After they broke the record, the Cre8 team were interviewed on TV. Imagine you are the interviewer. Write down five questions you would like to ask the hairdressers.

16 Mill Lane
Windton
East Sussex
BZ28 RRT

30 April 2011

Dear John Evans,

I am seven years old and in our class we are doing a topic on balancing. My dad told me that you have several Guinness World Records for which you have balanced objects on your head for over 10 seconds.

I have tried to balance a football on my head but it keeps falling off. I can't even balance a book on my head.

How did you learn to balance things? I read that you have balanced loads of things, such as crates, bricks, bikes, beds, boats, fridges and cars on your head.

My favourite record is heaviest car balanced on the head, in which you balanced a gutted Mini car on your head for 33 seconds. I can't believe it weighed 159.6 kg. Didn't your neck hurt? Is it true that you don't balance a car in windy places or on uneven ground? Why?

I hope you don't mind me asking all these questions. Keep on balancing and breaking more records.

Yours sincerely,
Imran

ON YOUR MARKS

a. What kind of car did John balance on his head?

b. Why do you think Imran finds it hard to balance a ball on his head?

c. How can you tell that this is a letter?

GET SET

a. What was Imran's favourite record?

b. Why do you think Imran wrote the letter?

c. Why do you think John doesn't like to balance a car when it is windy?

GO FOR GOLD!

a. Name two things that John has balanced on his head.

b. Is this a formal or informal letter?

c. Do you think John Evans is famous? Why?

BEYOND THE RECORD

Use the internet to find out more about John Evans. Choose one of his other records and write a newspaper report about his attempt. Remember to include the what, when, where, who, why and how.

Woodbridge Festival 2013

One of the BIGGEST summer music festivals in Europe!

CALLING ALL FESTIVAL-GOERS!

Fancy being a **GUINNESS WORLD RECORD** holder?

The music zone needs you!

On 1 August, we are going to try to break the world record for the largest orchestra playing on recycled materials. The current world record is held by 1,235 people and was organised by New Taipei City Government in New Taipei City on 23 June 2012.

Come and visit us in the music zone to find out more and sign up.

★ Have a go with our recycled instruments. They are made from objects such as oil drums, broken keyboards, typewriters, bread bins, metal road signs and metal pipes.
★ Join our workshops to explore ways of playing the instruments.
★ Get to know the musical piece we are putting together.

Let's show how important recycling is.

Let's break that world record!

ON YOUR MARKS

a. What world record is being talked about in this poster?

b. Why would oil drums make good instruments?

c. What do you think the orchestra will sound like when they play?

GET SET

a. What is Woodbridge Festival?

b. How does the poster make you want to come and join in?

c. Which recycled instrument would you choose to play? Why?

GO FOR GOLD!

a. How many people hold the current world record for the largest orchestra playing on recycled materials?

b. How would the workshops help players before the performance?

c. What two things is the poster trying to achieve?

BEYOND THE RECORD

Draw a design for your own recycled instrument. Use labels to show what it is made of, how it works and what sound it makes.

To: Thea

Cc:

Subject: I am a Guinness World Record holder!

Message Size: 379 KB

Image Size: Actual Size

Hi Thea,

Have incredible news! Remember this date – **12 May 2011** – because that's when I became a Guinness World Record holder. It's true.

Volunteers were needed to try to set a new Guinness World Record for the most people reading aloud simultaneously in one place. By the way, 'simultaneously' means at the same time.

So, on 12 May, my family and I caught a bus to the Malatya Inönü Stadium, Turkey, along with hundreds of other people.

When we arrived at the stadium, we were given a ticket and checked to see if we had the right book. Next, we were shown into the arena, where thousands of people were waiting. It was really noisy but very exciting.

Just then, someone asked for quiet and the whole stadium went silent. It was spooky.

After that, we all read the first chapter from *Les Misérables* by Victor Hugo, in Turkish. It sounded awesome.

Finally, as we walked out, we dropped our tickets into a box so they could be counted to see how many people had read.

So, the new world record is … **23,822! Hurray!**

Best wishes,

Habib

ON YOUR MARKS

a. How many people broke the world record?

b. How can you tell that this is an email?

c. What is the most interesting thing this email tells you about the day?

GET SET

a. What was the name of the book Habib read from?

b. Why do you think the reading sounded 'awesome'?

c. Why did Habib think it was 'incredible news'?

GO FOR GOLD!

a. What was Habib given when he arrived at the stadium?

b. Why do you think he found it suddenly 'spooky' in the stadium?

c. How well does Habib's email paint a picture of the day?

BEYOND THE RECORD

Research the Malatya Inönü Stadium on the internet. Produce a fact sheet about it. Find out about three other stadiums around the world and add the information to your fact sheet.

SUNFLOWERS

In the summer, look out for tall, yellow sunflowers in gardens and fields, following the sun. The tallest of these are giant sunflowers and, with the right care, they can grow very quickly.

GROWING ADVICE

Giant sunflower seeds need to be planted in a sunny place, in good, well-watered soil. It is also best to choose a spot out of the wind so that fully grown sunflowers won't get blown over.

A RECORD-BREAKING SUNFLOWER

CARE

Giant sunflowers are always thirsty and hungry, so they should be watered every day and fed special plant food. As they grow, some sunflower heads become so heavy that their stems need to be tied to a pole for support.

SUNFLOWER FACTS

- A sunflower head is made up of over 2,000 tiny flowers.
- The pith inside a sunflower stem is so light that it was once put inside life jackets.

RECORD-BREAKING SUNFLOWER

On 17 August 2009, a sunflower grown by Hans-Peter Schiffer in Kaarst-Voorst, Germany, broke the Guinness World Record for the tallest sunflower. At 8.03 m, it was taller than a double-decker bus!

ON YOUR MARKS

a. Who grew the world's tallest sunflower?

b. Why do you think sunflowers need special plant food?

c. Why do you think sunflowers 'follow' the sun?

GET SET

a. How tall was the world's tallest sunflower?

b. What do you think could happen to the stems of heavy sunflowers?

c. How does the layout of the text make it easy to find out how to grow and care for giant sunflowers?

GO FOR GOLD!

a. When and where was the world's tallest sunflower grown?

b. Why do you think sunflower pith was once put in life jackets?

c. What information did you find the most interesting? Why?

BEYOND THE RECORD

Use the information in the text to draw diagrams and captions to show how giant sunflowers are grown. Present your diagrams to the class and then hold a question-and-answer session.

LONGEST TONGUE

Tongue-tastic facts!

Your tongue has many important jobs. It allows you to chew, taste, swallow and talk.

Stand in front of a mirror and stick out your tongue. Your tongue is made of very strong muscles. The front, wiggly part can help you talk and chew food. The back part breaks down food to be swallowed, with the help of spit (also called saliva).

If you look closely, you'll see that the top of the tongue is covered in small bumps. These are taste buds, which allow you to taste sweet, bitter, salty and sour food and drink. You have up to 10,000 taste buds on your tongue.

Measure the length of your tongue from its tip to the middle of your closed top lip. It will probably measure 3–4 cm.

On 11 February 2009, a man called Stephen Taylor broke the Guinness World Record for the longest tongue. It was measured at 9.8 cm at the Westwood Medical Centre in Coventry, UK. In 2005, Stephen's tongue was 9.5 cm in length but he stuck his tongue out so much afterwards that it stretched!

Did you know ...?

- The blue whale's tongue can weigh as much as an elephant.
- Like fingerprints, everyone has a different tongue print.
- A difficult tongue twister is: The sixth sick sheikh's sixth sheep's sick.

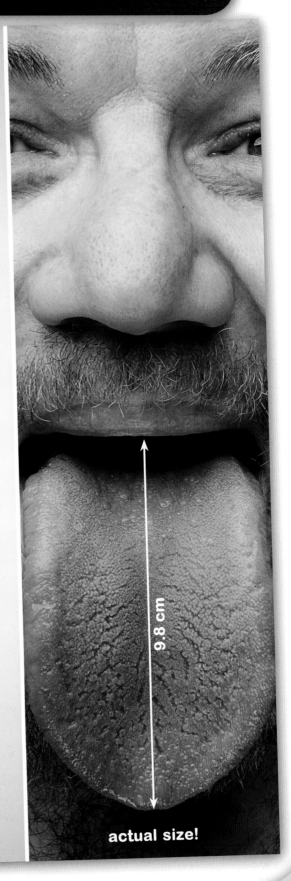

9.8 cm

actual size!

 ON YOUR MARKS

a. What four important jobs does a tongue do?

b. Why would you need a mirror to look closely at your tongue?

c. Why do you think the blue whale has such a huge tongue?

 GET SET

a. What is special about a tongue print?

b. Why do you think Stephen has stuck his tongue out so much since 2005?

c. What would you like to ask Stephen about his tongue?

 GO FOR GOLD!

a. How would you measure the length of your tongue?

b. Why do you think a tongue needs to be very strong?

c. Why is 'The sixth sick sheikh's sixth sheep's sick' a tongue twister?

 BEYOND THE RECORD

Use books and the internet to find out about two or three animals, insects or mammals who have long or large tongues. Find out why they have long tongues and how they use them. How will you record the information you find out: as diagrams with labels, or using bullet points?

33

6 November 2009

Tara:

Good evening. This is the news.

Dirk:

Have you ever made a human wheelbarrow? One person, who is the wheelbarrow, puts both hands on the ground, while the other holds the legs and pushes.

Well, this is *exactly* what hundreds of schoolchildren from Armidale in New South Wales, Australia, did today. As part of an official Guinness World Records day, they made an attempt to break the record for the largest human wheelbarrow race.

Tara:

When the starter went off, a huge crowd of human wheelbarrows made their way along the 50-metre course. Some were quick and others were slow. By the end of the race, a record-breaking 1,554 people — that's 777 wheelbarrows — crossed the finish line, making Armidale the new Guinness World Record holder. Glenda Wood, a teacher from Armidale, said that the children had been practising for weeks because they loved the idea of breaking a world record. She also thought it was a great way to bring local schools together.

Dirk:

Rather them than me, Tara! In other news ...

ON YOUR MARKS

a. How many human wheelbarrows broke the world record?

b. How long did the children practise for? What would you do to practise for this event?

c. Why do you think some went slowly in the race?

GET SET

a. In which country was the Armidale human wheelbarrow race held?

b. Why is there an explanation of a human wheelbarrow at the beginning of the news report?

c. Do you think a wheelbarrow race is an enjoyable way to set a world record? Why?

GO FOR GOLD!

a. At what speed did the racers move along the course?

b. Why do you think the event was 'a great way to bring local schools together'?

c. How do you know that the text is a TV news script?

BEYOND THE RECORD

If your school was planning an event like this, what would you need to think about to make sure it was well organised? Create a Mind Map™ to note your ideas.

Newsletter, 25 August 2008

Do you like skipping with a rope? Would you like to break a Guinness World Record?

Changi Bay School has been asked, along with other schools in the East Zone District, to take part in an event called the East Zone Skipping Challenge at Tampines SAFRA, on 29 August 2008.

The aim is to break the Guinness World Record for most people skipping together in one place, which at the moment is 3,009 skippers. To do this, all skippers must skip non-stop for three minutes.

To get ready for the event, we are running skipping lessons every day during and after school so that everyone can try it. Even the teachers are going to give it a go!

So let's get skipping! It's a great way to keep fit. You could learn a new skill and, who knows, you might even become a world record holder!

Newsletter, 1 September 2008

On 29 August 2008, a total of 3,105 people from 54 schools in the East Zone District of Singapore broke the Guinness World Record for the most people skipping at the same time.

Congratulations to all who took part!

ON YOUR MARKS

a. What are the children being asked if they like?

b. Why is 'let's get skipping' in larger letters than the surrounding text?

c. What is the 'East Zone District'?

GET SET

a. How is the school getting ready for the skipping event?

b. Why do you think 54 schools have been asked to take part?

c. Why does the author say 'you might even become a world record holder'?

GO FOR GOLD!

a. Write down three reasons why the children should take part in the skipping event.

b. Why is the school newsletter a good way of telling the children about the event?

c. Would you take part in this record attempt? Why?

BEYOND THE RECORD

Think of a fun club that could teach others in your class new skills such as skipping, hula-hoop twisting, street dancing or magic tricks. Create a poster to advertise the club. Include information about when and where the club takes place and why people should join.

www.bloggingforlife.com/Harry-Jupp42

MAR 12

March 12, 2012 15:33 GMT

*Posted by **Harry Jupp***

Ashrita Furman – my record-breaking hero

My mum knows how much I love reading the Guinness World Records books. So when she saw an article in the *Daily Telegraph* about Ashrita Furman, who is from the USA, she cut it out for me.

I had a look on Ashrita's website: **www.ashrita.com/**. Wow! This man is a record-breaking hero!

For a start, his records are really cool – things like underwater juggling and making the largest popcorn sculpture. And eating the most mashed potato in a minute. Yuck!

My favourite is the most forward rolls in one hour, which Ashrita broke in Kaliyakara, Bulgaria, on 8 January 2007. In just 60 minutes, he did 1,330 forward rolls over 2.11 miles. Doing all those forward rolls must have hurt, but Ashrita didn't give up.

On top of all that, since 1979 he has set over 400 Guinness World Records, including the 'most records held at the same time by an individual'. That's a lot of records!

I think he's a *real* hero. Can't wait to see what he'll do next.

Search

January

February

March

April

May

June

July

August

September

October

November

December

ON YOUR MARKS

a. Where does Ashrita Furman come from?

b. Why does Harry want to write about him?

c. Do you think Ashrita is a hero? Why?

GET SET

a. What is Harry's favourite record set by Ashrita?

b. Why does Harry write 'Yuck!' about eating the most mashed potato in a minute?

c. Why do you think practice helps people break records?

GO FOR GOLD!

a. Where did Harry find out about Ashrita Furman?

b. Why does Harry write in an informal way?

c. Do you think Ashrita's record attempts are fun? Why?

BEYOND THE RECORD

• Use Ashrita's website to find out more about the different Guinness World Records he holds.

• Choose your favourite record, then imagine you are going to try to break the record. Write a step-by-step training programme.

www.amazingmarathon.com/CarlCreasey

HOME / BIOGRAPHIES / NEWS / 2013 MARATHONS / USEFUL LINKS

Carl Creasey

If you watched the Virgin London Marathon on 17 April 2011, you may have seen a Royal Marine called Carl Andrew Creasey from the UK break the Guinness World Record for the fastest marathon carrying a 60-lb pack. He ran an incredible time of 4 hours, 50 minutes, 56 seconds.

A marathon is a long-distance running event – 26 miles and 385 yards long. More than 500 marathons are held in the world each year.

For most runners, a marathon is a huge challenge, even without having to carry a 60-lb pack! Carl says that he tried to break this world record because he wanted to test himself while running the marathon.

Every runner has to put in lots of training for a marathon. As Carl is a Royal Marine, he was already familiar with the Royal Marine commando course. He also went to the gym, swam, and trained with weights. He tried to run five days a week, and carried a bag with weights once a week.

Carl said that the hardest part of the marathon itself was coping with the heat. It was a perfect end to the race to be met by a man waving a certificate to say that he had broken the world record.

'With the right outlook, nothing is beyond you.' This is Carl's advice for anyone who would like to break or set a world record.

ON YOUR MARKS

a. Who broke the record for the fastest marathon carrying a 60-lb pack?

b. Why do you think Carl had to train so much?

c. How do you think Carl felt when he finished the race?

GET SET

a. How long did it take for Carl to finish the marathon?

b. Why was coping with the heat the hardest part of the marathon?

c. 'With the right outlook, nothing is beyond you.' This is Carl's advice for anyone who would like to break or set a world record. What would your advice be?

GO FOR GOLD!

a. Why was seeing a man with a certificate 'a perfect end to the race'?

b. What do you think is meant by 'With the right outlook, nothing is beyond you'?

c. Do you think breaking a world record is a good way to test yourself? Why?

BEYOND THE RECORD

The type of measurements used here are 'imperial' measurements. We now use 'metric' measurements. Can you complete this chart?

Imperial	Metric
60 lb	
26 miles, 385 yards	

41

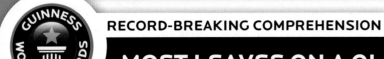

MOST LEAVES ON A CLOVER STEM

CLOVERS

Clovers are small green or purple plants that mostly have three leaves. There is a saying that if you find a four-leaf clover without looking for one, you will have good luck.

On 10 May 2009 Shigeo Obara found a 56-leaf clover in his garden in Hanamaki City, Iwate, Japan. This broke the Guinness World Record for the most leaves on a clover stem. A previous record for a 21-leaf clover was also held by Obara, but this new clover had 35 more leaves.

Shigeo Obara had been growing clovers since he found a few rare four-leaf clovers in 1951. He re-grew them in his garden, mixed them with other clovers and then noted down their different patterns, colours, sizes and numbers of leaves.

Before he wrote to Guinness World Records, Obara had to count all the leaves by sticking little number tabs onto each one. He must have felt very lucky when he saw so many leaves on just one clover.

ON YOUR MARKS

a. What do people say a four-leaf clover can bring you?

b. Why did Obara re-grow the four-leaf clovers in his garden?

c. Do you think Obara should have picked the clovers? Why?

GET SET

a. What colours can a clover plant be?

b. Why do you think Obara mixed clovers with other types of clover?

c. What sort of luck do you think Obara's 56-leaf clover might have brought him?

GO FOR GOLD!

a. What did Obara find in 1951?

b. How do we know that Obara loves growing clovers?

c. Why do you think Obara had to stick number tabs on the leaves?

BEYOND THE RECORD

Shigeo Obara kept notes about all his clovers to help him grow different types and sizes. Choose a plant that you can find outside. How will you capture information about this plant and how will you share this information with your friends?

Record-breaking 'Sling-back ears'!

Gently pull down your earlobe (the soft part of your ear) and then let it go. You will find that it will stretch and then bounce back – a bit like an elastic band. Monte Pierce, from Kentucky, USA, has pulled and tugged his earlobes so much that they have now become very stretchy, and extend to a length of 2.5 cm.

Monte doesn't mind having long, dangly earlobes because they have allowed him to break a very unusual Guinness World Record: the farthest ear sling-shot. Monte broke the record on 16 February 2008, when he appeared in front of an audience on the TV show *Lo Show dei Record* in Madrid, Spain.

Standing at one end of a large measuring mat, he carefully placed a 10 cent coin (about the size of a 5 pence coin) onto one of his huge earlobes. He then slowly stretched it down to almost 12 cm. Then, just like a sling-shot, he let go of his earlobe, causing the coin to travel a record-breaking distance of 3.55 m!

No wonder Monte's nickname is 'Sling-back ears'!

ON YOUR MARKS

a. Which part of the ear is the earlobe?

b. Why do you think Monte used a small coin?

c. Why do you think Monte's nickname is 'Sling-back ears'?

GET SET

a. What record did Monte Pierce break?

b. What does the word 'dangly' mean?

c. Why was a large measuring mat needed?

GO FOR GOLD!

a. Write down three adjectives that are used to describe Monte's earlobes.

b. Which paragraph recounts what happened on the show?

c. Do you think having a long earlobe helped Monte break the record? Why?

BEYOND THE RECORD

Imagine you were interviewing Monte on *Lo Show dei Record*. What questions do you think the viewers would like to ask? Make a list of five questions you would ask.

www.cyclefan/RezaPakravan

MAR 18 March 18, 2011 17:32 GMT
*Posted by **Cycle-Fan-No.1***

Reza crosses the Sahara

The Sahara Desert is the hottest desert in the world. This didn't stop Reza Pakravan from setting the Guinness World Record for the fastest crossing of the Sahara Desert by bicycle. It took him 13 days, 5 hours, 50 minutes, 14 seconds to cycle 1,734 km (1,083.85 miles).

Reza was born in Iran but lives in London. He spent six months planning for the trip: he had to train for four months and ask permission to cycle across the desert.

Each day during the trip, Reza ate 6,000 calories and drank 7 litres of water. He cycled along desert tracks and in the evenings he camped or stayed with local tribes.

Reza faced many problems along the way, such as flies, flat tyres and strong sandstorms. He arrived safely in Sudan on 17 March 2011.

'It was an amazing experience,' said Reza, looking back on his record-breaking ride.

Reza's kit list:
- special bike
- food ration packs
- water
- bike repair kit
- map
- camping equipment.

Essentials for breaking this record:
- GPS tracking device for tracking position and direction
- daily log
- evidence: signatures of important people who saw Reza pass by
- evidence: photographs at important places.

ON YOUR MARKS

a. What desert did Reza cycle across?

b. How much water did Reza drink each day, and why?

c. Why do you think it would be hard to cycle in the desert?

GET SET

a. How long did it take Reza to cycle across the desert?

b. Where was he cycling to, and how do you think he felt when he got there?

c. What is evidence? Why do you think Reza needed evidence?

GO FOR GOLD!

a. Name three problems Reza faced in the desert.

b. How do you think Reza kept going in such a difficult environment?

c. Give two reasons why Reza needed to train for four months.

BEYOND THE RECORD

Search the internet for a film of Reza crossing the desert. Then write a travel blog imagining you are cycling in the Sahara Desert. A sandstorm is heading your way. Describe the storm and how you feel.

LONGEST JOURNEY BY POWERED PARAGLIDER

PARAGLIDING

Benjamin Jordan, a photographer from Canada, had always wanted to fly. One day his dream came true when he tried paragliding.

 Breaking records

 Above and beyond

In 2009, Benjamin decided to link his love of photography and flying in a special way. He planned to set the Guinness World Record for the longest journey by powered paraglider by flying 10,000 km across Canada.

Benjamin set off on 15 May 2009 from Tofino, British Columbia. Along the way, he visited 50 youth camps and schools to talk about his journey. As he left, the children would often stand together to make shapes for Benjamin to see from above. Some children made the shape of a whale and others made the letters 'Don't quit'.

On 24 August 2009, Benjamin finally landed at Bay St Lawrence (Nova Scotia). He had flown 8,008 km, setting a new Guinness World Record.

His photographs of the journey were made into a book called *Above and Beyond*. The profits of the book were used to pay for children from low-income families to go to summer camp. *Above and Beyond* not only made Benjamin's dreams come true but also those of many children.

ON YOUR MARKS

a. What is Benjamin Jordan's job?

b. Why do you think he used a powered paraglider?

c. What do you think the author wants you to feel about Benjamin?

GET SET

a. What record did Benjamin Jordan break?

b. Why would Benjamin be a good person to talk to about following dreams?

c. Why do you think the book was called *Above and Beyond*?

GO FOR GOLD!

a. How many youth camps and schools did Benjamin visit?

b. Why do you think one group of children made the message 'Don't quit'?

c. How do you think the journey made some children's dreams come true?

BEYOND THE RECORD

Think of ways you could raise money for a good cause or charity by trying to break or set a Guinness World Record. Use a Mind Map™ to record your ideas. What would you do? Where? How? When? Who would be involved? Present your ideas on a poster to show to the class.

The Pooh Room

Rose Conti

Deb Hoffmann lives near Waukesha in Wisconsin, USA. From the outside, her two-storey house looks like all the others. But once you're inside, it's clear that one of the rooms is very special.

Deb calls it the 'Pooh Room' because it stores her huge collection of Pooh and Friends objects. In fact, it's so huge that on 15 July 2011 Deb set the Guinness World Record for the largest collection of Pooh and Friends memorabilia. A staggering 5,150 objects were counted.

> **Memorabilia:** objects about someone or something.

Over the years, Deb has collected Pooh-related toys, clothes, books, DVDs, puppets, posters, mugs and many other things.

It started when she fell in love with a Pooh phone. She says that although it was hard to find, she 'kinda liked the rush of the hunt'. After that, she trawled through garage sales, charity shops, internet sites and stores for Pooh objects. She hasn't stopped since.

As the sun sets, the jam-packed 'Pooh Room' glows yellow. At some point, I guess Deb will need another room for her ever-growing collection because, as she says, 'Now I want them all!'

ON YOUR MARKS

a. Where does Deb Hoffmann live?

b. Why do you think she may need another room?

c. Would you like to visit the 'Pooh Room'? Why?

GET SET

a. What made Deb Hoffmann start her collection?

b. How would a sunset make the room 'glow yellow'?

c. What does the verb 'trawled' mean?

GO FOR GOLD!

a. Which adjective suggests that the room is very full?

b. Why do you think Deb wants more Pooh and Friends memorabilia?

c. What do you think Deb means when she says she 'kinda liked the rush of the hunt'?

BEYOND THE RECORD

Do you have a collection? How would you present this to friends? If you don't collect anything, what would you like to collect and how would you start your collection?

THE SHANDONG TIANYU MUSEUM OF NATURE

LINYI, PINGYI COUNTY, SHANDONG PROVINCE, CHINA

Welcome to our world-famous museum for dinosaurs and prehistoric fossils. Built in 2004, this huge museum covers 28,000 square metres and is home to 1,106 dinosaur objects and thousands of fossils. Awarded the Guinness World Record on 22 July 2010 for the largest museum devoted to dinosaurs and prehistoric fauna, it is a great way to spend the day.

Wander through the 28 different rooms and stare with wonder at the dinosaur skeletons. Discover your favourite dinosaurs and find out how they lived. Keep an eye out for the world's largest example of the dinosaur, *Sinosauropteryx*.

Marvel at the fossil of a worm's tiny egg, or the fossil of a bird feather.

Stroll through magical halls that show the most beautiful stones in the world, such as China's largest diamond, and sparkling crystals from South America.

With all of this and a 4D cinema, the Shandong Tianyu Museum of Nature is a place you will never forget.

Come and see this amazing collection of young *Psittacosaurus* dinosaur skeletons.

ON YOUR MARKS

a. What is the name of the museum?

b. Write down two verbs from the text that mean 'to walk'.

c. Which part of the museum would you like to visit? Why?

GET SET

a. What is the museum devoted to?

b. What are 'dinosaur objects'?

c. Why would you 'marvel at the fossil of a worm's tiny egg'?

GO FOR GOLD!

a. Give two reasons why the museum is 'a place you will never forget'.

b. What are 'prehistoric fauna'?

c. Why do you think the museum has used pictures on the leaflet?

BEYOND THE RECORD

Use the internet to find out more about the Shandong Tianyu Museum of Nature. How would you persuade somebody to visit?

Shanghai Party for *Jin Mao* Tower Record Breakers

The Jin Mao Tower in Shanghai, China, is one of the highest buildings in the world. Standing at 420.5 m tall, with 88 floors, it would be hard work to walk up, but imagine cycling up! This is exactly what three extreme cyclists decided to do.

The record for most steps climbed by bicycle was achieved on 31 December 2007 by Zhang Jincheng from China, Xavi Casas from Andorra and Javier Zapata from Colombia. It took them 41 minutes, 57 seconds to climb 2,008 steps.

Stair climbing by bicycle is a difficult skill. The three cyclists had to stand up on their bikes and then bounce from step to step. To make it harder, they could not touch the ground, wall or any other part of the building with their bodies.

The cyclists explained that they had two reasons for taking part. One was to set a Guinness World Record and the other was to welcome in 2008, the year of the Beijing Olympics in China.

A big party was held afterwards to celebrate what they had achieved. What a fantastic way to welcome in the New Year!

▲ You need skill and control to stair climb by bicycle.

ON YOUR MARKS

a. Where is Jin Mao Tower?

b. What do you think is the hardest part of stair climbing by bicycle? Why?

c. Why did the cyclists choose the Jin Mao Tower?

GET SET

a. Why is stair climbing by bicycle a 'difficult skill'?

b. Why did the cyclists climb 2,008 steps?

c. Why do you think the Chinese people wanted to give the three cyclists a big party?

GO FOR GOLD!

a. What were the two reasons for cycling up the tower?

b. What do you think 'extreme cyclist' means?

c. Why would it be hard for the cyclists not to touch the ground, walls or any other part of the building?

BEYOND THE RECORD

Find out more about the extreme sport of stair climbing by bicycle. Two of the cyclists have other records for stair climbing. What makes them want to do it? How do they train? What kind of bikes do they use?

READING SKILLS

There are different skills you need to learn when reading texts.

Each AF (assessment focus) describes a different set of reading skills. In this book, you will actively practise and improve your ability to do the following.

AF2:

- Find information in a text.
- Find evidence in a text.

AF3:

- Understand what the writer means but does not tell you directly.

AF4:

- Find patterns in a text.
- Comment on organisation of texts.

AF5:

- Understand why the writer chooses a word.
- Understand why writers sometimes use very short sentences.
- Comment on how a writer uses language for effect.

AF6:

- Identify the writer's purpose.
- Understand the writer's viewpoint and the overall effect of the text.